MMM, DELICIOUS!

Chapter 25
Coffee Time Confrontation!

OH, LEONIE. AS LONG AS YOU HAVE SOME KIND OF TORTE, YOU COULDN'T CARE LESS WHAT IT'S PAIRED WITH.

PFFT!!

YUM. NOTHING BEATS A CUP OF COFFEE AFTER LESSONS.

TORTE GOES SOOO WELL WITH BLACK TEA.

...SO PARTICULAR AM I ABOUT MY TORTE!

DON'T BE ABSURD!

WHY, I COULD NOT SURVIVE WITHOUT THE TORTE FROM THIS BAKERY...

FWOOSH

THEY HAVE A ROYAL WARRANT OF PATRONAGE, THEN?

I ALWAYS HAVE MY TORTE ORDERED FROM THE SAME BAKERY.

MY, MY...

TSK, TSK, TSK. NOT SO!

5

KÖNIGLICHE FAMILIE LEHRER

Higasa Akai

CONTENTS

KÖNIGLICHE FAMILIENLEHRER

BEING ON THE LIST GIVES A BUSINESS THE RIGHT TO USE THE ROYAL COAT OF ARMS.

THE KINGDOM OF GRANZREICH KEEPS A LIST OF ROYAL WARRANT HOLDERS.

ONLY THE KING MAY ELECT TO ALTER THE LIST.

I SEE...

THEY CAN'T HAVE JUST ANY OLD ROYAL FIDDLING WITH THE LIST.

IT'S A HIGHLY-PRIZED PRIVILEGE FOR SHOPS.

I DO SO LOVE COFFEE!

IF I WERE KING, THEN, I SUPPOSE I'D PICK CAFÉ KLAUS, THE PLACE THAT SELLS THIS COFFEE BLEND.

HEH HEH!

OHHH...

IF I WERE KING, I WOULD ABSOLUTELY GIVE THIS TORTE A "ROYAL WORRUNT."

DO YOU NOT REALIZE WHAT IT MEANS TO BE A PRINCE?

YOUR FREE-WHEELING WAYS ARE UNACCEPTABLE!!

BECAUSE IT'S BOUND TO BE A PAIN. ESPECIALLY IF BRUNIE FINDS OUT.

THAT IS TYPICAL OF HIM.

TCH. A WASTE OF MY EFFORTS, THAT STUDENT.

QUITE TRUE...

OH? WHY NOT?

PSST

MMBL

OH, YEAH. TEACH.

MY BROTHERS CAN'T KNOW I WORK AT THE CAFÉ, OKAY?

DON'T GET IT

I'M STILL LEARNING. I WANT TO MAKE THE DRINKS AT THE CAFÉ SOMEDAY...

OH, UH...

I MUST ADMIT, I DID NOT KNOW THAT YOUR HIGHNESS COULD BREW COFFEE.

SO SOMETIMES I LET MYSELF IN HERE TO PRACTICE.

I SEE...

GRIND GRIND GRIND GRIND

GRIND

...SINCE I HAVE FATHER'S PERMISSION TO BE THERE ANYWAY, I WANT TO LEARN MORE OF THE JOBS AT THE CAFÉ.

...I'VE BEEN THINKING SINCE WHAT HAP-PENED, AND...

IS IT JUST ME, OR ARE YOU AWFULLY PRACTICED AT THIS...?

FLINCH

CIRCLE
CIRCLE

......

UH!

Y-YOU KNOW! LADIES LOVE THIS SORT OF THING!

THE PALACE BUTLER

I THOUGHT THIS WAS A BUTLER'S JOB.

TH-THAT WAS CLOSE...

OH. IS THAT HOW IT IS...?

....

...YOU DO ENDLESS RESEARCH INTO HOW TO KEEP THE LADIES HAPPY, YOU SEE!

WHEN YOU'RE AS POPULAR AS I AM...

THERE YOU ARE. ENJOY.

THANK YOU.

POKE
POKE
つん
つん

ARE YOU SURE THIS WILL TASTE GOOD...?

THE FLAVORFUL AROMA AND ACIDITY ARE WELL-BALANCED.

......!

IT IS DELICIOUS.

RIGHT? RIGHT?

POKE つん つん POKE
POKE つん
....
POKE つん つん POKE
POKE つん つん POKE
POKE つん
POKE つん つん POKE

IT'S MY ORIGINAL BLEND, MADE WITH LOVE!

I USED COLOMB AND ABYSSINIAN BEANS, WHICH AREN'T VERY BITTER.

CAUTIOUS

FWOO... FWOO...

...I SUPPOSE I CAN GIVE IT A TRY...

I-IF YOU SAY IT WILL BE GOOD...

BWAAAH! HOW DO I GET LEONIE TO DRINK COFFEEEE?

......

GLOOM

YOU CANNOT CHANGE OTHERS' TASTES, AND I CANNOT RECOMMEND FORCING ANYTHING UPON HIM.

PERHAPS IT IS TIME YOU YIELDED?

......

Kaiser Melange

BUT OF COURSE, THE OMNIPOTENT PROFESSOR HEINE WOULD EVEN BE AN EXPERT ON VARIOUS COFFEE DRINKS.

WHAT-EVER YOU SAY.

NATURALLY.

I HAVEN'T THE FOGGIEST NOTION WHAT YOU COULD MEAN.

HEH.

I LET YOU MAKE ME DANCE IN THE PALM OF YOUR HAND.

I AM, AFTER ALL, A REGULAR CUSTOMER AT A MOST SPLENDID CAFÉ.

I JUST HAD A GREAT IDEA!

?

OH!

......

STARE

Hidden Bonds

GH...

NNH...

タッ
TUMP.

PRINCE KAI!

HE LOOKS TO BE IN A GREAT DEAL OF PAIN.

......

I HAVE FINISHED EXAMINING PRINCE KAI.

I... SINCERELY WISH I DID NOT HAVE TO TELL YOU THIS...

WHILE IN THE GARDENS, HIS HIGHNESS ATE SOME BERRIES THAT HAD FALLEN TO THE GROUND...
...AND UNFORTUNATELY, THEY SEEM TO HAVE GIVEN HIM INDIGESTION.
A DAY OF BED REST SHOULD BE ENOUGH TO SEE HIS HIGHNESS RETURNED TO FULL HEALTH.
PLEASE TAKE CARE.
SCUTTLE
KACHAK
パタン…

GOODNESS. BUTTON UP YOUR SHIRT.

KEEP THE BLANKET AROUND YOUR SHOULDERS.

FWFF もう

FWFF もう

HOW-EVER... ...IT IS NOT RIGHT, CAUSING UNDUE STRESS FOR EVERYONE IN THE PALACE.

...SORRY.

MN...

NOW, YOU WILL STAY IN BED AND MAKE A SWIFT RECOVERY.

UNDER-STOOD!?

GOOD LORD, THAT TROUBLE-MAKER...!

HE DOES NOT REQUIRE MY ATTEN-TION.

YOUR VISIT IS OVER ALREADY?

LET US BE OFF, MASTER!

IT WAS BUT A FALSE ALARM.

ぷんす FUME

ぷんす FUME

ぷんす FUME

·········

THE TEXT FOR TOMORROW'S GROUP LESSON... SHOULD I GIVE IT TO PRINCE KAI, GIVEN HIS CONDITION?

I WOULD PREFER THAT HE RECEIVE IT TODAY...

....

JUMP

PRINCE BRUNO.

WHAT SEEMS TO BE THE MATTER? YOU HAVE BEEN STANDING BEFORE PRINCE KAI'S DOOR.

M-MASTER!

COULD IT BE YOU ARE WORRIED?

...

44

......?

BECKON
BECKON
クイ
クイ

...SORRY,
BRUNO.

!

IF IT
MAKES
YOU
SAD...

...I WON'T
DO THINGS
THAT MAKE
YOU WORRY
ANYMORE...

IT'S
ALL ON
ME. THIS
TIME AND
THAT TIME
BOTH.

I'M
FINE...

Chapter 27
Adele's Friend

GOOD LORD. YOU'VE GONE AND INCONVENIENCED MASTER AS WELL...

—AND SO, WE ARRIVE AT THE PRESENT.

KAI. COME HERE...

LEONHARD.

BECKON

BECKON

...NOT AT ALL. IN FACT, I AM INCLINED TO SAY THAT I AM PARTIALLY RESPONSIBLE...
THAT PICTURE...

I-I'M SORRY... I WAS UPSET, AND BEFORE I KNEW IT...

WHAT IS THE POINT OF GIVING IN TO ADELE'S TANTRUM AND BRINGING HER TO THE ZOO?

...I APOLOGIZE FOR THE BOTHER.

P.S. THEY HAVE GUARDS ALONG TOO.

*IN PLAINCLOTHES!

MOREOVER, YOU WOULD LIKELY NOT HAVE BEEN GRANTED PERMISSION TO LEAVE THE PALACE WITHOUT A CHAPERONE.

ROGER!

YES, MASTER!

FWIP

PRAY TAKE THE UTMOST CARE NOT TO REVEAL YOURSELVES.

ALTHOUGH THE ZOO IS FAR FROM CROWDED, IT IS CERTAINLY NOT DEVOID OF ORDINARY VISITORS.

ENJOYING THIS VISIT TO THE ZOO WILL CALM HER, I'M SURE.

I BELIEVE THAT WAS MERELY HER TEMPER SPEAKING.

...DOES ADELE TRULY INTEND TO FIND A NEW PLAYMATE?

...ME TOO.

THE ZOO... FUN...

ALL RIGHT! THEN I SHALL SEE TO IT THAT ADELE HAS AS MUCH FUN AS POSSIBLE!

TEACH, YOU JUST HAVE TO TURN EVERYTHING INTO A LESSON, DON'T YOU?

A SPLENDID IDEA. I TOO AM PLEASED FOR THE OPPORTUNITY TO TEACH YOUR HIGHNESSES HOW TO DEAL WITH ANIMALS.

......

OR, IT COULD BE THAT A MUTATED VARIETY OF GIRAFFE WITH LONG NECKS WAS BORN, AND THEIR KIND OUTLIVED THOSE WITH SHORTER NECKS. THERE ARE SEVERAL SUCH THEORIES.

ONE THEORY IS THAT THE GIRAFFE EVOLVED A LONGER NECK FOR THAT VERY PURPOSE.

NOW...

OBSERVE THE GIRAFFE, PLEASE.

DO YOU SEE HOW HE EATS LEAVES FROM A TALL TREE?

TSK, TSK, LEONIE! EVOLUTION TAKES MILLIONS AND MILLIONS OF YEARS. IT'S A DREADFULLY SLOW CHANGE.

AHA!!

STRETCH

THEN...THEN WHAT IF I WISHED TO EAT TORTE THAT WAS LEFT ON A TALL SHELF?

BADUM

BADUM

PRINCE LICHT, COME HERE FOR A MOMENT.

I SEE...

IF IT WERE THAT FAST, DON'T YOU THINK TEACH WOULD BE TALLER BY NOW?

*TEDDY BEAR

O-OKAY, OKAY, YOU DON'T HAVE TO GET INTO FULL LESSON-MODE TODAY.

ITS NATURAL HABITAT IS ON THE EASTERN CONTINENT. AS AN OMNIVORE, IT USES ITS PAWS AND CLAWS TO CATCH PREY—

THIS IS A BLACK GRIZZLY BEAR, A SUBSPECIES OF THE BROWN BEAR.

SNARL

GROWL

B-BUT BEARS ARE MUCH SCARIER THAN I IMAGINED!

LOOK. YOU HAVE WORRIED HER...

WERE YOU NOT GOING TO SEE TO PRINCESS ADELE'S AMUSEMENT?

LEO? ARE YOU OKAY...?

THEN NEXT, TO LIFT YOUR HIGHNESS'S MOOD, LET US OBSERVE A SMALL AND GENTLE ANIMAL.

HMPH.

THE PRINCESS...

...MUST LOOK TO HER OWN HEART.

PRINCESS ADELE.

NO? THEN WHAT, PRAY TELL, WOULD YOU MAKE OF THAT?

SIR SHADOW WISHES TO SEE YOU.

N... NUH-UH... I DON'T BELIEVE YOU...

YOU'RE MY VERY BEST FRIEND!

I'M SORRY! I'M SORRY, SHADOW!

OH... YOUR FAVORITE TOY...?

YOU WANT TO PLAY WITH ME?

CLUNK

SO SHE'D MAKE UP WITH SHADOW?

YOU BROKE THE TOY, DIDN'T YOU?

WHISPER

...HEY, TEACH.

I NEED TO ASK YOU SOMETHING.

WAVE WAVE

WHAT, THEN SHADOW HONESTLY BROKE IT?

BUT HE'S A DOG!

SORRY, SORRY!

HMPH!

I WOULD NEVER DO SOMETHING SO HORRID.

YOU WOUND ME!!

...HAD IT NOT BEEN MOVED, THE PRINCESS COULD VERY WELL HAVE BEEN IN DANGER...

HYPOTHETICALLY, IF IT WAS LEFT NEXT TO A LIT CANDLE...

...APPEARED TO HAVE A SMALL SCORCH MARK ON ITS CANVAS.

...BUT NOW THAT YOU BRING IT UP, THE CAUSE OF THEIR SPAT— THAT IS, THE PORTRAIT I DREW...

YOU COULDN'T BE SUGGESTING THAT...

Y...

PLOD

PLOD

PLOD

H-HE'S A HERO!!!

WOOF!

A-ARE YOU HUNGRY?

SIR SHADOW?

HOW MUCH DOES THAT DOG KNOW?

FROM THEN ON, THE PRINCES TOOK TO ADDRESSING THEIR PET DOG AS "SIR SHADOW," WITNESSES SAY.

Chapter 28
The Price of the Past

MASTER...

KAI...

BUT OF COURSE. FOR HIS MAJESTY THE KING IS ALSO COMMANDER OF THE ARMY.

ROYAL TUTOR.

TO SUCCEED THE THRONE, A PRINCE MUST HAVE MILITARY EXPERIENCE.

YOU ARE AWARE OF THIS REQUIRE-MENT?

......

......

?

IT IS TIME YOU KNEW OF IT.

...UNTIL A PARTICULAR INCIDENT ONE YEAR AGO.

...IT WAS CUSTOMARY FOR GRANZREICH'S PRINCES TO ATTEND MILITARY ACADEMY BEGINNING AT THE AGE OF FIFTEEN...

IN ADDITION TO SCHOOLING BY A ROYAL TUTOR...

THIS TABLOID WAS RELEASED THIS MORNING.

"A TABOO TOPIC KEPT SUPPRESSED BY THE ROYAL FAMILY...

"THE TRUTH ABOUT THE SECOND PRINCE'S VIOLENT RAMPAGE—"

"ONE YEAR AGO, WHEN PRINCES KAI AND BRUNO WERE STILL ATTENDING MILITARY ACADEMY...

"...THE PRINCES USED THEIR POSITIONS AS ROYALS TO KEEP THE WHOLE SCHOOL UNDER THEIR THUMBS.

"THEY THREATENED EVEN THE INSTRUCTORS, FORCING THEIR TEACHERS TO GIVE THEM TOP MARKS DESPITE NEVER ATTENDING THEIR LESSONS OR TRAINING EXERCISES.

"OUR SOURCES SAY THAT THEY VICIOUSLY BEAT ANYONE WHO DEFIED THEM.

"THIS IS THE INCIDENT THAT BROUGHT HIS VIOLENT TEMPER INTO THE PUBLIC EYE.

"PRINCE KAI WAS RESTRAINED AT THE SCENE.

"BUT THE NIGHTMARE FINALLY CAME TO AN END AFTER ONE 'STUDENT R' WAS FOUND WITH SERIOUS INJURIES.

"YET TO THIS DAY, THE REST OF THE PRINCES' TRANSGRESSIONS REMAIN A WELL-KEPT SECRET.

"HE CONTINUES TO SUFFER UNDER PRESSURE FROM THE STATE."

"...BUT STUDENT R, THE VICTIM, WAS PUNISHED WITH EXPULSION.

"HELD ACCOUNTABLE FOR THIS FIGHT ALONE, PRINCE KAI WAS SUSPENDED FROM THE ACADEMY, AND PRINCE BRUNO TOOK A LEAVE OF ABSENCE...

IT WAS THE MOST PREVALENT STORY I UNCOVERED DURING MY RESEARCH BEFORE I ARRIVED AT THE PALACE.

......

THE FIGHT PRINCE KAI WAS INVOLVED IN...

YET UPON MEETING THE PRINCE, IT SEEMED SO UNLIKE HIM THAT I DISMISSED IT AS NOTHING BUT A RUMOR.

MASTER.

THAT ARTICLE IS COMPLETE NONSENSE.

...BUT...

I-I UNDERSTAND THAT... BUT STILL...

OUR PEOPLE HAVE THE RIGHT TO FREE SPEECH.

IT IS OUR DUTY TO PROTECT THAT RIGHT, NO MATTER WHAT THEY CHOOSE TO BELIEVE.

THE VERY IDEA...IF I COULD CRUSH THE ENTIRE NEWSPAPER COMPANY...

100

BRUNO.

THAT WOUND...

WITH THE SAME PERSON AS BEFORE?

NO, NO, DO NOT MISINTERPRET. MY OWN LACKLUSTER SWORDSMANSHIP WAS THE CAUSE...

AH, THIS...

...HAPPENED DURING TRAINING.

...BRUNO...

...ARE YOU HAVING... PROBLEMS?

NONE WHATSOEVER.

YOU WORRY FAR TOO MUCH, BROTHER.

CLINK

THIS HAPPENED SEVERAL MORE TIMES, UNTIL ONE EVENING...

BRUNO'S LATE... WHAT'S KEEPING HIM?

HE'S USUALLY THE ONE WAITING AT THE CARRIAGE FIRST.

HOW LONG IS HE GOING TO BABYSIT THE PRINCE?

HE SAYS IT'S STILL NOT ENOUGH.

AH-HA-HA-HA! SERIOUSLY?

THE TRAINING HALL... IS HE STILL PRACTICING...?

CREAK

ROYAL TUTOR... LOOK AFTER THESE TWO FOR ME.

YOUR MAJ-ESTY.

......

...UNDER-STOOD.

......

KCHAK

......

CONFOUND IT...THEY WROTE NAUGHT BUT UTTER NON-SENSE...

AND WE CAN DO NOTH-ING!

...BRUNO, DO YOU KNOW... WHERE "STUDENT R" LIVES?

HUH...? WELL, ONLY NOBLES ATTEND THAT MILITARY ACADEMY.

I AM SURE WE COULD FIND OUT...

JUMPING TO CONCLUSIONS...IS WRONG.

WHY, HE IS MORE THAN LIKELY THE ONE BEHIND ALL OF THIS HOGWASH!

KNOWING WHAT HE DID...HE IS CERTAINLY NOT THE KIND OF PERSON WHO WOULD SO EASILY CONCEDE!

...BUT I'VE ALWAYS WANTED TO KNOW WHY HE HURT YOU.

HE WAS OFFICIALLY PUNISHED...

...NH!

I NEED TO BE ABLE TO TALK WITH ALL KINDS OF PEOPLE...

TEACHER, WHAT DO YOU THINK?

BUT FATHER SAID TO WAIT...

...IF I WANT TO BE A CANDIDATE FOR THE THRONE...

!!!!

......

MM...

WE ARE READY TO DEPART, PRINCE KAI.

......

PLEASE DO NOT MISUNDERSTAND HIM...

...I BELIEVE THAT, FOR MY BROTHER, THAT WAS A "SMILE FROM EAR TO EAR."

Y-YES, OF COURSE!

......

AH HA HA HA HA!

OH, QUITE!

YOU COULD SAY THAT HIS AWKWARDNESS IS, ERM, A CHARM OF HIS!

AH HA HA HA HA!

AH HA HA HA HA!

MM...

I ASK THAT YOU WAIT INSIDE THE CARRIAGE FOR THE TIME BEING.

IT IS POSSIBLE THAT HE HARBORS A GRUDGE TOWARD YOUR HIGHNESS.

LUDWIG AND I WILL GO ALONE...

...TO NEGOTIATE A PLACE TO SPEAK WITH HIM.

HERR FUCHS, ARE YOU THERE?

KNOCK KNOCK

WHO ARE YOU?

......

CREAK

A CHILD...?

CLAMP
むくっ

I'LL HAVE YOU KNOW, I AM A FULL-GROWN—

P-PERHAPS IT WOULD BE BEST TO SAVE THAT FOR LATER...

むすっ
FUME

むすっ
FUME

FLINCH
ビクッ

WE ARE ENVOYS FROM THE PALACE.

...I AM.

I APOLOGIZE FOR CALLING SO SUDDENLY. ARE YOU RALF VON FUCHS?

CREAK
...I...
I HAD LITTLE OTHER CHOICE MYSELF.
I KNOW I CAN'T ASK YOU TO TRUST ME... BUT...
...IF PRINCE KAI IS HERE, I WANT YOU TO LET ME MEET WITH HIM.
I WANT TO TELL HIM EVERYTHING... AND APOLOGIZE IN PERSON.

Chapter 29
Future Salvation

HUH? WASN'T LUDWIG SUPPOSED TO BE WAITING FOR US INSIDE? '''

HE NEEDED TO FRESHEN UP AND LEFT WITH A SERVANT.

THIS BOY FUCHS...THE STUDENT WHO ATTACKED PRINCE BRUNO...

HE FOUGHT WITH PRINCE KAI AND WAS SUBSEQUENTLY EXPELLED FROM MILITARY ACADEMY...

......

HERE. YOU MAY PLAY WITH ONE OF MY YOUNGER BROTHER'S TOYS.

LET ME SEE... WILL YOU BE PLAYING IN THE GARDEN?

HE LOOKS TO BE A RATHER SUBDUED YOUNG MAN TO MY EYES...

WHA ....!?

HRMPH

THAT'S OUR PROFESSOR.

ALWAYS BEING MISTAKEN FOR A CHILD......

I AM A GROWN MAN AND A TEACHER.

NOW, WE WISH TO HEAR WHAT YOU HAVE TO SAY ABOUT THE INCIDENT.

......

...BUT TO ATTACK PRINCE BRUNO. WHAT DID YOU MEAN BY THIS?

AT THE DOOR, YOU SAID THAT YOU HAD "LITTLE OTHER CHOICE"...

I THINK IT ALL STARTED WHEN I HEARD THOSE RUMORS.

RUMORS?

SQUEEZE

I FELT AS THOUGH I COULD DO NOTHING ELSE... THAT IS...

I WASN'T THINKING STRAIGHT... I...

......

138

!

THAT ROYALS DO WHATEVER THEY PLEASE AT THE ACADEMY AND ARE NEVER DISCIPLINED FOR IT.

THAT THEY ARE PLACED AT THE HEAD OF THEIR CLASS NO MATTER WHAT GRADES THEY TRULY EARN.

AND I WAS NEVER THE TOP STUDENT IN MY CLASS...

THAT'S BECAUSE... BRUNO IS SMART AND ALWAYS MINDFUL OF HIS CONDUCT...

AND I'D NEVER SEEN AN INSTRUC- TOR REBUKE HIM...

IT IS TRUE THAT HE...HIS HIGHNESS PRINCE BRUNO, WAS THE TOP STUDENT IN HIS CLASS.

I KNEW THAT...THAT THEY WERE ONLY RUMORS.

BUT...

EVEN THE INSTRUCTORS HELD BACK AROUND PRINCE BRUNO.

HE MIGHT NOT HAVE REALIZED IT, BUT EVERYONE ELSE SAW IT.

...BUT THE FACT OF THE MATTER IS, PRINCE BRUNO WAS ONLY ABLE TO REACH THE TOP OF HIS CLASS...

...BECAUSE HE GREW UP WITH A SUPERIOR EDUCATION IN THE FIRST PLACE...!

UNTIL WE...

...WE GOT MORE AND MORE RILED UP.

AS MY FRIENDS AND I WERE DISCUSSING IT...

......

I WON'T ASK FOR YOUR FORGIVENESS.

......

......?

...DO YOU KNOW... ABOUT THIS...?

A PAPER FROM THIS MORNING...

...HAS AN ARTICLE... ABOUT THE INCIDENT...

SHFF

...WH-WHY, THIS IS ALL NONSENSE!

...I...

...WANT THEM TO CORRECT THE LIES IN THIS ARTICLE.

I REMEMBER NOW... A REPORTER CAME BY THREE DAYS OR SO AGO.

HE SAID HE WANTED TO ASK ME ABOUT THE INCIDENT.

I TURNED HIM AWAY. I HAD NO IDEA HE'D DONE THIS...

WE ONLY TOOK YOU IN FOR YOUR MANSION.

YANK

IF YOU REALLY WANT TO JOIN OUR "FAMILY," YOU'D BETTER PROVE YOU'RE WORTH IT.

DON'T GET COCKY, BOY.

I WON'T LET YOU DOWN!

I'LL USE THOSE MUGS TO SQUEEZE A FORTUNE FROM THE ROYAL PALACE! I SWEAR IT!

......

WE'LL STAY UP HERE AND HELP OUR- SELVES TO A ROUND OF DRINKS.

DON'T MESS UP.

YES, SIR!

JANGLE

JANGLE

WOOOW...
WHAT A BIG
CELLAR...IT'S
A MAGNIFICENT
MANSION...
EVEN UNDER-
GROUND...

HRMPH!

....

WE'VE
KILLED
HIM
OFF?

I DO
WONDER
WHAT'S
BECOME OF
HIM....

HEY
YOU!...

DON'T
SAY THAT!
I'D FOLLOW
YOUR
HIGHNESS TO
THE ENDS OF
THE EARTH
TO PROTECT
YOU!

MY LATE
MENTOR
WOULD'VE
WANTED
ME TO!

SORRY...THIS
IS ALL BECAUSE
I SAID I WANTED
TO TALK TO
HIM...

ZWISH

!

......

STROKE

I'M UNDER ORDERS NOT TO DAMAGE OUR MONEY-MAKER ANY MORE THAN NECESSARY...

...BUT A PRINCE TREMBLING IN FEAR WOULD MAKE FOR A FANTASTIC PHOTO-GRAPH.

TCH!

DOESN'T EVEN FLINCH...

......

PRINCE KAI!

WELL, THEN... ...DOES THIS SCARE YOU?

YANK

!!

...KH!

CLENCH

......!

STOP...!

......NH.

SMASH

"—HEINE.

"I WANT YOU TO PROMISE ME ONE THING."

...ULP!

SLUMP

"BUT IF EVER MY SONS ARE IN DANGER...

"YOU WILL KEEP THE OLD YOU SLUMBERING IN THE DEPTHS OF YOUR HEART.

"...THEN YOU MAY......"

A TEACHER'S ROD IS NEVER TO BE USED IN SUCH A SAVAGE MANNER.

SQUEEZE

GRAB

SWISH

D-DAMN YOU...!

SWISH

PANG

SPROIIING

みろ————ん

...I CERTAINLY CANNOT BEHAVE VIOLENTLY FOR ANY REASON OTHER THAN SELF-DEFENSE.

AFTER PRINCE KAI WORKED SO HARD TO STAY HIS HAND...

BE GRATEFUL TO HIS HIGHNESS.

...WHAT ARE YOU LOOKING AT?

......

IT'S NOT AS IF I WAS RISKING LOSING ANYTHING IN THE EVENT WE WERE CAUGHT.

I WAS ALREADY ALONE...

......

...ONE DAY...

I BET YOU'RE DREADFULLY PLEASED TO SEE ME BEING DRAGGED AWAY, AREN'T YOU!?

HOLD YOUR TONGUE, YOU LOUSE!

ONE DAY, YOU SHOULD COME WORK AT THE PALACE.

YOUR HIGH-NESS!?

...COME AGAIN?

......

YOUR HIGHNESS! UMM, WHAT ARE YOU SAYING?

HE WAS HOLDING US FOR RANSOM NOT A MOMENT AGO!

IF YOU'VE GIVEN UP ON JOINING THE MILITARY... IT'S THE BEST PLACE...TO PUT ALL OF YOUR STUDIES TO USE...

...YOU SHOULD TRY TO JOIN THE PALACE GUARD.

...WHEN YOU'VE PAID FOR YOUR CRIME...

COME ALONG, NOW.

TUG

......

FROM WHOM DID YOU FIRST HEAR THE RUMORS IMPLICATING THE ROYAL FAMILY?

MAY I MAKE ONE INQUIRY OF YOU?

...I'M NOT OBLIGATED TO GIVE YOU AN ANSWER.

......

I SHOULD MUCH LIKE TO KNOW, ASSUMING THAT WAS NOT ANOTHER LIE.

...I THINK... IT MAY HAVE BEEN AN ACQUAINTANCE OF MY PARENTS...

THEY FINALLY PUBLISHED A CORRECTED ARTICLE, DID THEY?

SHUT

AS WORD OF FUCHS'S ARREST SPREADS...

...THE PRINCES' ILL REPUTE SHOULD IMPROVE NATURALLY.

...COUNT ROSEN-BERG...

IMPRESSIVE INDEED, ROYAL TUTOR.

...YES. THERE IS NAUGHT TO WORRY ABOUT.

DOES IT SEEM AS THOUGH THIS BUSINESS WITH PRINCE KAI WILL HAVE A HAPPY ENDING?

I HAD A FEELING YOU WOULD COME HERE.

FWOOOO

THIS IS A LITTLE STORY THAT TOOK PLACE LONG BEFORE PROFESSOR HEINE CAME TO THE ROYAL PALACE...

TREMBLE

TREMBLE

IT'S REALLY LOUD...I'M SCARED...

FWOOOO...

RATTLE

RATTLE

RATTLE

LICHT, SIX YEARS OF AGE

CLENCH

MAYBE I SHOULD GO TO FATHER'S ROOM AND ASK TO SLEEP WITH HIM...

189

WHY NOT BE CHILDISH... ONCE IN A WHILE...?

GOOD MORNING, BROTHERS...

MMM...

...NH...

TWEET

TWEET

The Royal Tutor, Vol. 6
Coming March 2018!

OH, THE SUSPENSE!
WHAT WILL THE PROFESSOR AND THE COUNT DISCUSS...?
MORE CHARMING ROYAL TUTOR,
COMING SOON.

The Royal Tutor ❺

Higasa Akai

Translation: Amanda Haley • Lettering: Abigail Blackman

THE ROYAL TUTOR Vol. 5 © 2015 Akai Higasa / SQUARE ENIX CO., LTD. First published in Japan in 2015 by SQUARE ENIX CO., LTD. English translation rights arranged with SQUARE ENIX CO., LTD. and Yen Press, LLC through Tuttle-Mori Agency, Inc., Tokyo.

English translation © 2018 by SQUARE ENIX CO., LTD.

Yen Press
1290 Avenue of the Americas
New York, NY 10104

Visit us at yenpress.com
facebook.com/yenpress
twitter.com/yenpress
yenpress.tumblr.com
instagram.com/yenpress

First Yen Press Print Edition: January 2018
The chapters in this volume were originally published as ebooks by Yen Press.

Yen Press is an imprint of Yen Press, LLC.
The Yen Press name and logo are trademarks of Yen Press, LLC.

Library of Congress Control Number: 2017938422

ISBN: 978-0-316-48007-9

10 9 8 7 6 5 4 3 2 1

BVG

Printed in the United States of America